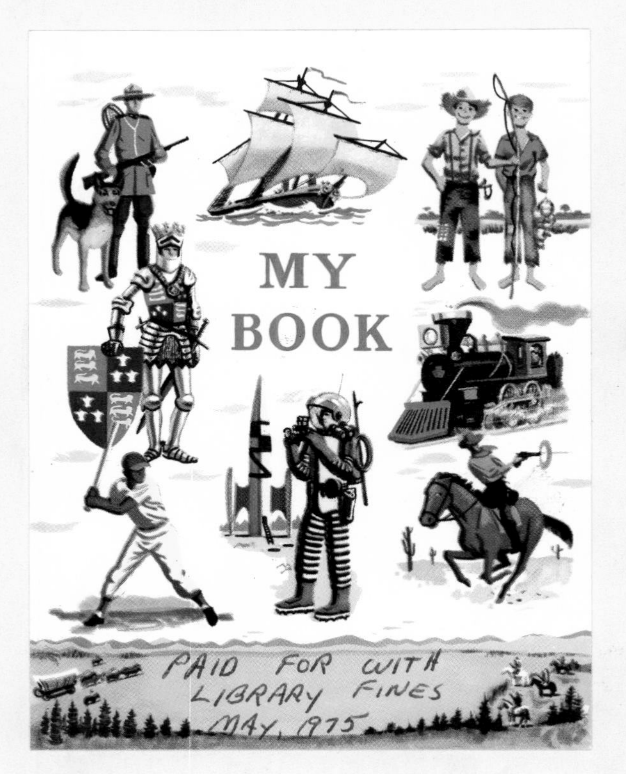
MY
BOOK
PAID FOR WITH
LIBRARY FINES
MAY, 1975

D1265857

IF YOU HAVE A YELLOW LION

Also by Susan Purdy

MY LITTLE CABBAGE
Mon Petit Chou

CHRISTMAS DECORATIONS FOR YOU TO MAKE

IF YOU HAVE A YELLOW LION

SUSAN PURDY

J. B. LIPPINCOTT COMPANY
Philadelphia and New York

for my
mother and father

Printed in the United States of America

Library of Congress Catalog Card Number 66–11014

IF YOU HAVE A YELLOW LION

All the colors you have seen

You can make, including green.

To start you only need a few:

Black, white, yellow, red, and blue.

It's fun to mix new colors.
From all these just pick two,
And paint them on an animal
To brighten up your zoo.

If you have a yellow lion,

And you try to paint him red,

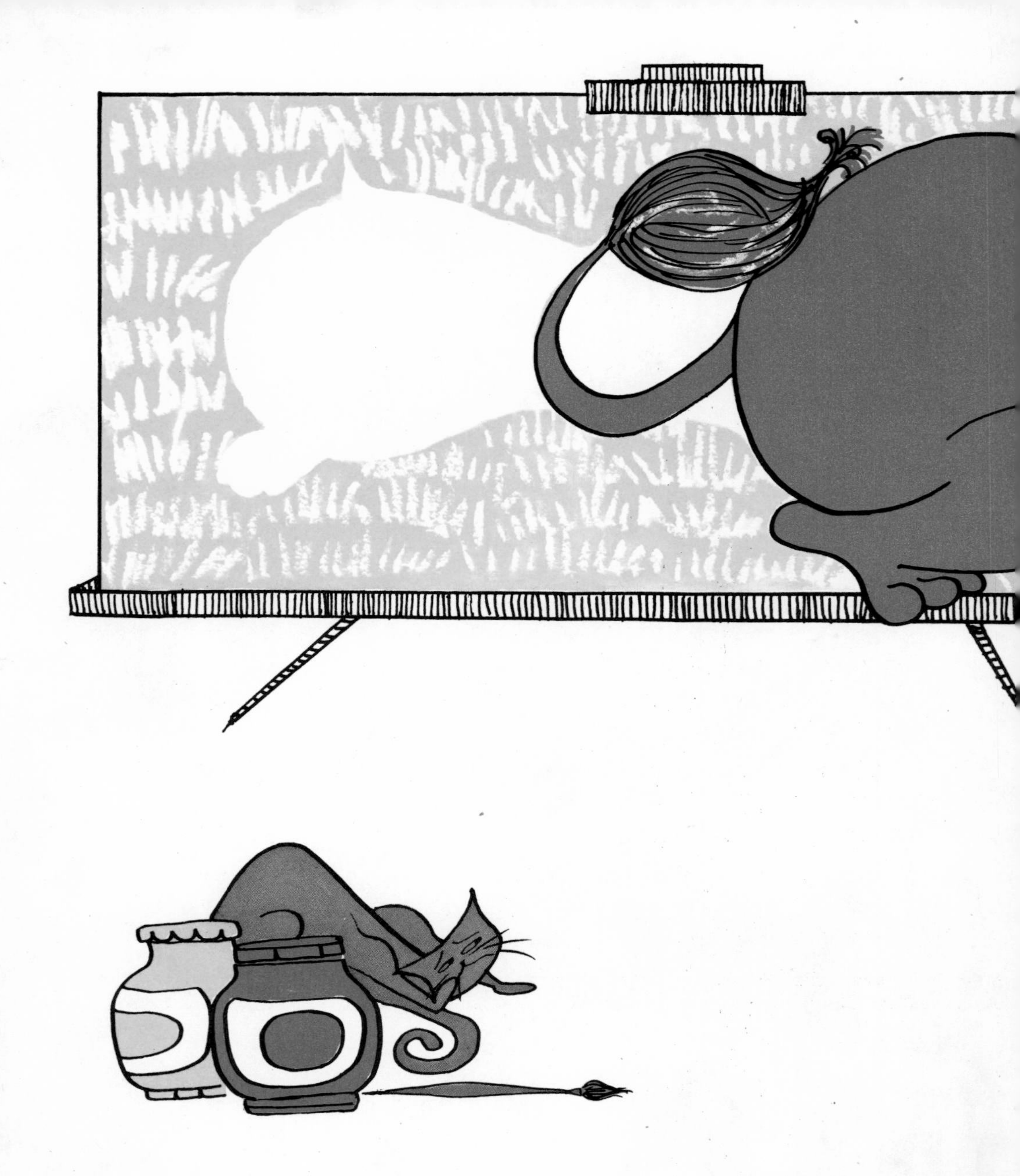

You may be quite surprised to find

That he's turned orange instead.

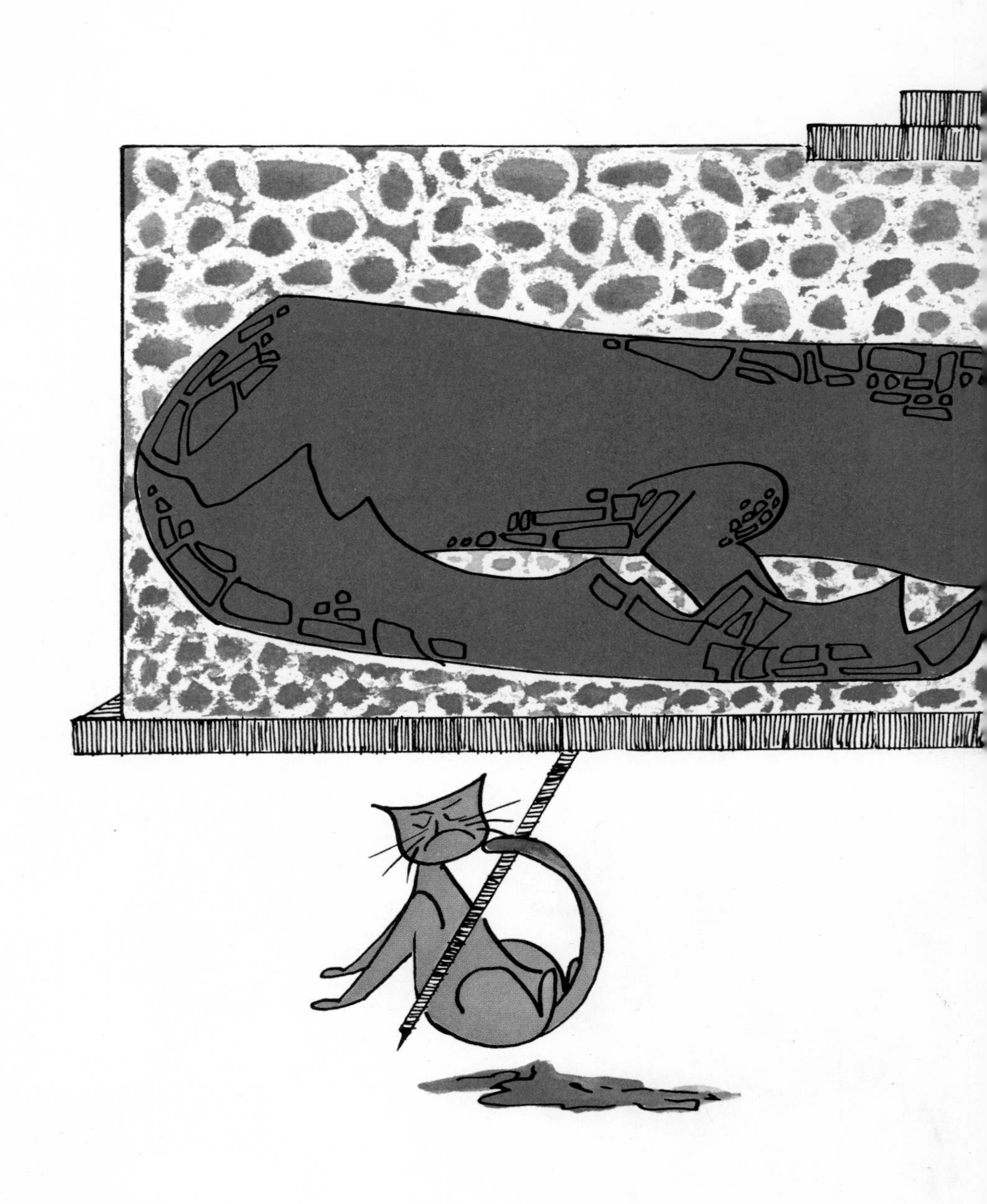

If your crocodile is looking blue,

Paint her with some yellow, too.

She'll be as happy as a queen

To see you've turned her color green.

If your old bird could use some paint,

Try mixing red and blue.

For purple on a pelican

Is something very new.

If you have a monkey

Who thinks that he's a clown,

Try mixing all three colors

And painting him with brown.

To stripe your zebra black and white,

Don't let the colors run.

Or you will turn your zebra gray,

And he won't think it's fun.

If your colors are too bright,

Just add some white

To make them light.

Black makes colors dark, my friend

And that's the time to say

The end.